GLACIER
SKYWALK

Walk out onto the ice / Go ahead / I know you all want to / take with you a breath of air / a clenched stomach /

an eye for what you cannot see / and a hand to hold / for this is not what your mother taught you / she'd never allow you...

...to go out there / and when the wind / calls you at the back / of your neck / and the blood rushes to your head /

with how alive you feel on the platform / it will be her voice you hear / for that brief moment / before your whole body /

feels as if it now somehow / belongs here / connected to the planet

"INTO AIR" BY DEREK BESANT

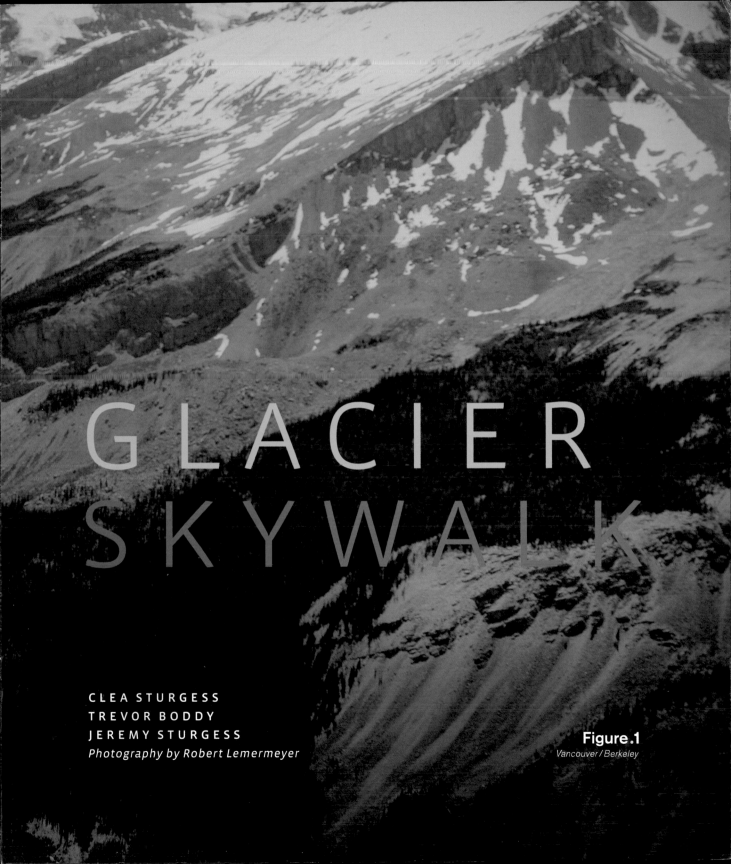

GLACIER
SKYWALK

CLEA STURGESS
TREVOR BODDY
JEREMY STURGESS
Photography by Robert Lemermeyer

Figure.1
Vancouver / Berkeley

pp. ii–iii Athabasca Glacier, 1924.
pp. iv–v Icefields Parkway, Jasper National Park, Alberta.
pp. vi–vii Sunwapta Valley, Jasper National Park, Alberta.

CONTENTS

INTRODUCTION
CLEA STURGESS / JEREMY STURGESS

OVER THE SUNWAPTA VALLEY, in the heart of the
Rocky Mountains and at the apex of the Great Divide,
a man-made structure balances from the edge of a cliff
to give an unprecedented view of glacier, mountains
and valley.

Virtually invisible from the Icefields Parkway,
Glacier Skywalk's cantilevered glass-floored walkway
inspires simultaneous terror and delight when visitors
realize they are suspended over a precipice with no
visible structural support. This is the climax of a journey
that winds its way along the mountainside, with stops
that interpret, hide and reveal the astonishing natural
surroundings.

The project began in the fall of 2010, when Brewster
Travel Canada asked teams of engineers, architects
and contractors to compete to create a vision for a new
attraction on a site in Jasper National Park. Parks Canada
had precipitated the idea for this competition through
a call to companies like Brewster to envision new

attractions that would encourage tourists to get out of the car and embrace nature and the realities of climate change.

The primary goals were to manifest the structure into a man-made extrusion of the landscape and to weave a series of macro experiences that would link the 300-metre distance from the bus stop to the Skywalk bridge as a journey in itself.

The competition process, the scale, the context and the unprecedented type of building inspired innovation and cooperation from all members of the team. The site offered a rare combination of natural setting to capture visitors' interest and imagination, rich cultural and ecological history to inform the design and provide interesting learning opportunities, and previously developed land to minimize the impact of new construction.

The process that ensued was an extraordinary collaboration of client, Parks Canada and government personnel, consultants, contractors and manufacturers, each one a champion for what had become the project of a lifetime. This is the story of that process. //

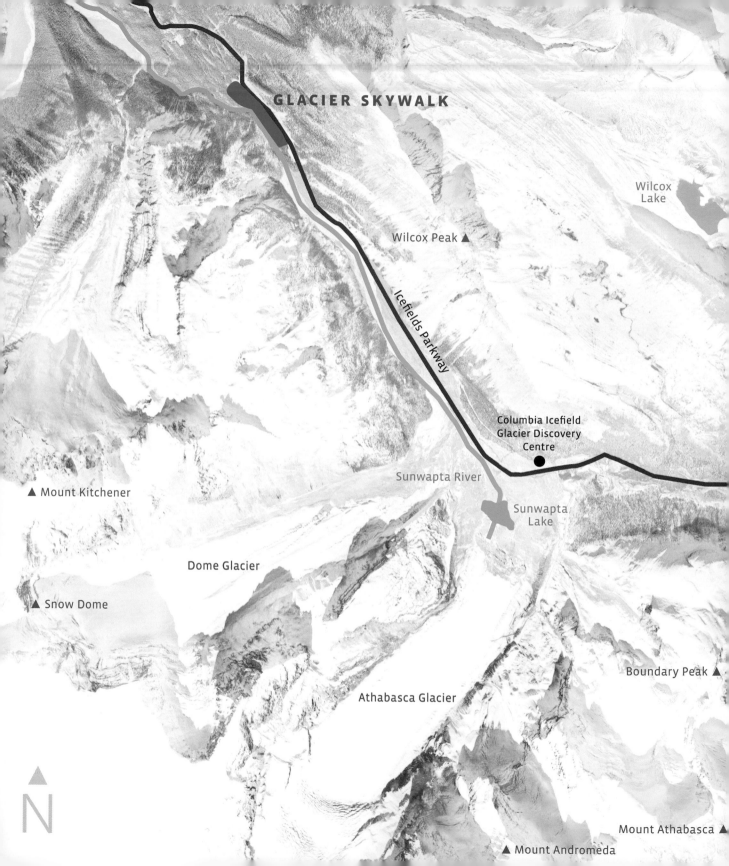

GLACIER SKYWALK

Wilcox
Lake

Wilcox Peak ▲

Icefields Parkway

Columbia Icefield
Glacier Discovery
Centre

Sunwapta River

Sunwapta
Lake

▲ Mount Kitchener

Dome Glacier

▲ Snow Dome

Boundary Peak ▲

Athabasca Glacier

Mount Athabasca ▲

N

▲ Mount Andromeda

First Skywalk

IT WAS THE LAST DAY THAT Glacier Skywalk was open before winter closing. As a writer on architecture, I knew of its mounting design awards and had marvelled at photographs of its rust-coloured steel projections framing a walkway of sheer glass. But it was clear to me that so sculpted and unique a creation could never be captured by images alone. I knew that Glacier Skywalk—above all other architectural creations—needed to be experienced in person.

To do so I had driven all that October day from Edmonton, across the plains swept by showers, then up into the verdant first ridges of the foothills, evergreens speckled with daubs of aspen clutching their last chrome-yellow leaves. Things brightened under the laser-crisp alpine light west of Rocky Mountain House; of all the driving I have done on five continents, the transition into the mountains from there, or west out of Calgary or Lethbridge, is by far the most dramatically scenic. Entering into the embrace of the Rocky Mountains' craggy peaks always has a strong impact on me, as I still consider the mountain parks my spiritual home. I spent some teenage summers at what was then the Banff School of Fine Arts, and for many years after was drawn back to the area's hiking and ski trails. As I descended the last miles of the David Thompson Highway en route to the Icefields Parkway, my destination, I recalled during those long-ago days hearing the rumble of ice falling from the glacier while camping, and standing in front of the greenish waters of Peyto Lake for my favourite family portrait.

The Brewster operations centre and parking for Glacier Skywalk tours lie right off the parkway. As I arrived, I grabbed my camera and jacket and dashed into the ticket lobby, praying I had not missed the last bus up. I had. A staffer, however, offered to drive me to Glacier Skywalk in his own car. On the way up, we talked of the weeks of work ahead preparing the Skywalk bridge and its flanking pavilions for winter snows and storms. Not until we were approaching the drop-off did I remember how steep and vast is the Sunwapta Valley here at the boundary of Jasper National Park.

I was dropped next to a kiosk, the only real building on
site. With the enormously deep valley spread out behind it,
this kiosk clad in larch boards was somewhat reassuring.
The wood here harked back to the rustic national park–style
pavilions every Rockies visitor comes to love, but it was shaped
into triangular facets, its walls transforming into benches.
Rounding the corner of the kiosk towards the Skywalk itself,
I felt a moment of immense power—terror and delight in
fulsome mixture. Partly this was the full effect of gazing
down into the valley and seeing the rawness of its rock-strewn
slopes. But just as much of what overwhelmed here was a
string of human creations: two levels of pathways meandering
along the cliffside, framed by rocks boxed into metal mesh
bins; a sequence of odd metal constructions punctuating
the route; and at the end, the thrusting steel knives of the
Skywalk bridge itself, its glass decks glinting in the late-day
autumnal sun. Expecting a walk in the park, I instead found
an impassioned battle between nature and culture.

I tried to make sense of the forms I was seeing. From
my perspective, the angled flanks and tapering ends of the
Skywalk looked like a scout ship crafted by some alien intelli-
gence hovering over the valley. It was wrapped in a weathered,
irregularly marked steel, its forms now seeming as much
geological syncline and shale outcropping as rocket wings
and deflector shields. Strangely, I found myself forgetting the
Skywalk and instead investigating the series of other metallic
pavilions, or call them glacial erratics, along the path. One of
them was a miniature Skywalk, an intergalactic rowboat to

its larger tender hovering nearby. Walking out onto its shorter cantilever over the valley foreshadowed the main construction, but in a very poetic way.

Sci-fi and geology both failing as means of understanding, I tried music: the similarities of shape and function between this first and the second—much larger—deck were like those exquisite little leitmotifs in the first sections of Wagner's *Ring Cycle* that expand into orchestral majesty in the later operas. From there I looked directly across the valley and saw a portion of the glacier clinging perilously to the bare rocks of the mountaintop. This prompted me to think of Richard Strauss's *An Alpine Symphony,* which played in my head right through the remainder of my visit. I only glanced at the didactic panels explaining and illustrating the flora, fauna and geology of the area, but found myself staring, enraptured, at the metallic constructions surrounding them.

With the light soon to fade, I wanted to revel in this combination of place and architecture. I walked halfway down to the main Skywalk entrance, where a thick grid of the rust-coloured Cor-ten steel structure was wrapped in more Cor-ten to form a gateway. Feeling an eerie implication of weight while passing under the gateway's mass and structure, I intuited a lesson in the principles of mountain building. Arriving at the start of the Skywalk bridge, I was surprised to find an asymmetrical loop. ("The engineers must have gone crazy!" I muttered to myself.) Cautiously, I strode along the long side of the loop, then paused at the very end to look in all directions, including through the floor, then looped back along the shorter walkway. It is hard to capture in words the combined senses of fear and wonder that I felt hovering over that Rocky Mountain valley, but it was different to all of my hiking, skiing and flying around this part of the world. Pausing there also reminded me why mystics contemplate mountains to clear the heart and mind.

I emerged, after doing the glass-floored circuit, at another woodsy construction, a sister form to the kiosk and similarly covered in larch boards. It was a place to sit, a relief, I imagine, for guests unused to this altitude and a perfect spot to take in this saturation of gravity and the surrounding sights. At times it also doubles as an amphitheatre. It seemed an entirely appropriate way to come back to terra firma after visiting the cosmos.

At closing time, I caught the last tourist bus of the year for the ten-minute trip down to the parking lot where I'd left my car. An older Korean couple sitting across from me smiled broadly, communicating what their tongues could not. A few words of greeting in Portuguese to a klatch of young Brazilians prompted an avalanche of praise for this crisp northern world, with its rocks, ice blocks, conifers and extraordinary bridge out into the void. And several Canadian and Australian hotel-workers—who had been hearing about Skywalk all summer from their guests— declared their joy in experiencing the structure for themselves. I returned to my car reflecting on how Skywalk had touched us all. For me, edgy and inspired architecture had enriched a place I thought I already knew. //

Designing The Skywalk

FOR AN ARCHITECT, there is no more difficult design problem than to shape a building for a spectacular natural site. The beauty of nature can be inspiring, but it can also be intimidating for the designer. Cities and towns—with their patterns of roads and previous buildings—provide immediate clues for the architect in setting essential forms. Not so a lush forest, a stretch of desert or a boulder-strewn mountain slope. Responding to the power of nature, some architects largely bury their creations in the soil

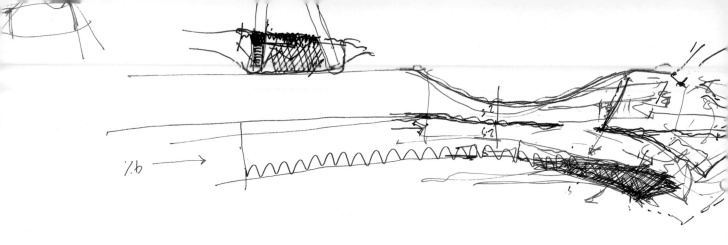

(as with many early passive solar houses), but the ground above them is never the same. Others adopt curving, supposedly organic forms (as with recent work by the "blob architects"), but these often result in the most alienated and intellectual impositions. There are virtues in using a palette of materials from the place or region, but walls of shining horizontal logs are not a forest, and bricks made from local clay are predictable instruments of regularity.

Designing successfully for a natural site requires a rare balance of humility and assertiveness, openness to the visual cues of a site but also the strength to impose the mental logic of contemporary built forms upon these places. The most thrilling quality about Sturgess Architecture's design for Glacier Skywalk—even more thrilling than the views its construction affords—is its sequence of pavilions upon a landscape, forms in rusting steel and wooden boards that seem both eternal and newer than new. These pavilions, or nodes, have different shapes because they reveal different themes and ideas latent in each of their locations. To understand how Glacier Skywalk came to be, we must first understand how its design team was formed, what sources inspired their creations and how these ideas developed into a sequence of architectural designs on this lonely ledge in the Rocky Mountains.

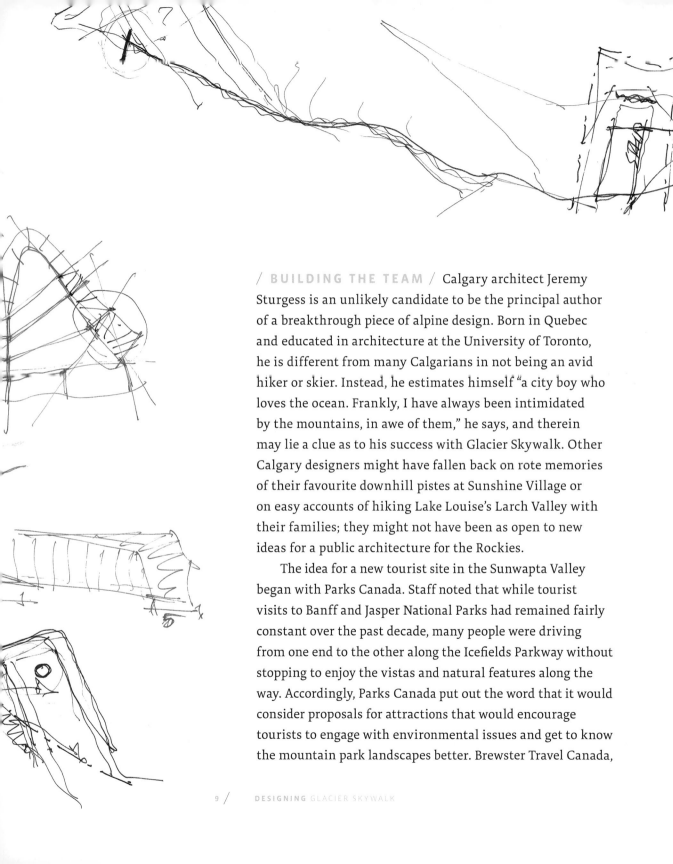

/ **BUILDING THE TEAM** / Calgary architect Jeremy Sturgess is an unlikely candidate to be the principal author of a breakthrough piece of alpine design. Born in Quebec and educated in architecture at the University of Toronto, he is different from many Calgarians in not being an avid hiker or skier. Instead, he estimates himself "a city boy who loves the ocean. Frankly, I have always been intimidated by the mountains, in awe of them," he says, and therein may lie a clue as to his success with Glacier Skywalk. Other Calgary designers might have fallen back on rote memories of their favourite downhill pistes at Sunshine Village or on easy accounts of hiking Lake Louise's Larch Valley with their families; they might not have been as open to new ideas for a public architecture for the Rockies.

The idea for a new tourist site in the Sunwapta Valley began with Parks Canada. Staff noted that while tourist visits to Banff and Jasper National Parks had remained fairly constant over the past decade, many people were driving from one end to the other along the Icefields Parkway without stopping to enjoy the vistas and natural features along the way. Accordingly, Parks Canada put out the word that it would consider proposals for attractions that would encourage tourists to engage with environmental issues and get to know the mountain park landscapes better. Brewster Travel Canada,

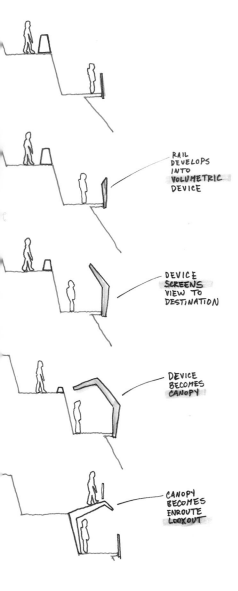

RAIL
DEVELOPS
INTO
VOLUMETRIC
DEVICE

DEVICE
SCREENS
VIEW TO
DESTINATION

DEVICE
BECOMES
CANOPY

CANOPY
BECOMES
ENROUTE
LOOKOUT

Sectional sketch studies.

a company that has been operating buses, tours, hotels and attractions in Canada's Rocky Mountain parks for more than a century—including seasonal tours across the top of the nearby Columbia Icefield glacier—took up the challenge.

In consultation with Parks Canada staff and environmental and design professionals (architects, engineers, naturalists, museum specialists), Brewster prepared a proposal call for companies to design and build what it was then calling "Glacier Discovery Walk," a glass-floored observation deck like the popular tourist attractions operating in Dubai and the Grand Canyon that suspend visitors above stunning vistas. The proposed site was an existing viewpoint on the Icefields Parkway, but it was evident early on that direct car access to the pull-off would create too many logistical problems. Instead, Brewster envisioned visitors parking, purchasing tickets and having access to services at its existing Columbia Icefield centre, and then being taken by bus to the Skywalk ten minutes away. A guide would provide information en route, and once at the drop-off, visitors would walk down the gentle slope and past a variety of displays to the bridge, where they could experience the dramatic valley and mountain views.

Brewster put out the proposal call in the fall of 2010. Because Skywalk would be a complex piece of engineering in a sensitive location, Brewster invited integrated teams of architects, engineers and builders working together to craft a complete design–build package. Along with other Alberta contracting firms, PCL Construction Management—

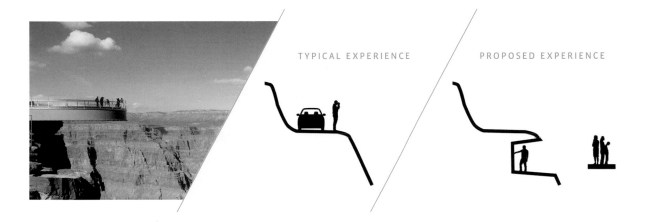

TYPICAL EXPERIENCE

PROPOSED EXPERIENCE

LEFT Grand Canyon Skywalk, Flagstaff, Arizona. Photo courtesy of Sturgess Architecture
RIGHT Tourist experience as described by Parks Canada.

one of the largest construction firms in the country—began to assemble its team. The Brewster commission was small by PCL's usual standards, but it would be high profile. For the crucial role of structural engineers, PCL chose Read Jones Christoffersen (RJC), a large firm with a huge range of complex jobs under its belt and one of PCL's frequent collaborators. Both companies had a sense it would take a powerful design to win this prestigious commission, and RJC thought Sturgess Architecture, a much-lauded design-oriented firm with whom it had worked on projects ranging from housing and public buildings to Calgary's Seventh Avenue light rail transit stations, fit the bill precisely. Important to the task at hand, Jeremy Sturgess (and his partners Lesley Beale and Kevin Harrison) had excelled at a number of innovative buildings in Alberta's mountains: Squirrel Corner, Banff's first courtyard housing project; some private houses in Bragg Creek, Banff and Canmore; a renovation and addition to the Post Hotel in Lake Louise; and especially Banff Town Hall. These last two, in particular,

are updates on the beloved rough-hewn national park–style wooden architecture produced in both Western Canada and the United States in the late nineteenth and early twentieth centuries.

According to Sturgess, "Design–build is by definition a scary undertaking for architects" because it locks in a barely schematic design concept for years, everyone knowing it needs to be constructed for a fixed price. For smaller firms such as Sturgess Architecture, competitions can be a risk that puts a burden on staff and finances. The entire team knew that features first proposed in the design stage would need to evolve as new information and constraints emerged in the build phase, and that editing of the design—called value engineering in the construction business—would have to occur. That said, Sturgess sees some advantages to team building in this technique: "Design–build can also create a wonderful sense of buy-in [with building and engineering partners] working together with the architects to maintain the most essential features," enforcing overall integrity when the inevitable changes need to be made.

/ DEVISING THE CONCEPT / With PCL as builders, RJC as engineers and Sturgess as architects, the team was in place to enter Brewster's design–build competition. All were aware that a bold design concept was crucial—but what should its themes or ideas be? Quite early on, the Sturgess architects devised two central design concepts that informed their initial sketches and carried right through the entire finished construction. The first of these essential architectural ideas for Glacier Skywalk is material and tactile, the other spatial and narrative.

A strategy for composing Skywalk's structure, material palette and colour arose very early on, after Jeremy Sturgess drove the three hours from his Calgary office to the site and took in the stupendous views up and down the Sunwapta Valley. These first visits to future building sites are one of the most important stages of an architect's creative process, because understanding the play of topography, light, vegetation and other natural features helps to form, then further, design ideas. On some rocks below the viewpoint, he noticed rust stains and rust-coloured lichen, and, looking up, he saw thin streaks of the same rust-red iron oxide amongst the geological layers across the bare rock faces framing the valley. Sturgess almost immediately hit on the building material that would match this colour: Cor-ten steel, a metallic plate product with a somewhat irregular oxidized surface. More importantly, Cor-ten is incredibly strong, he thought, and can be cut, formed or welded into almost any shape; and requires no painting or preserving over the years (see page 15).

STEEL

COR-TEN STEEL was chosen as the cladding material for structural elements and as the architectural finish for the kiosk and the pavilions (nodes). Not only do its greys and deep reds mirror the iron deposits of the local mountains (and change in hue and character over time, as do the mountains), but it is structurally strong and versatile enough to use in walls, roofs, trusses, fins and ledges that extend irregularly from the mountainside like the fractured geological plates in the surrounding landscape. As it is already unevenly marked from the milling process and seals itself when scraped, Cor-ten is forgiving and maintenance-free. / *c.s.*

Near the red-stained rocks, Sturgess also noted evidence of calcification, quartz-like translucent deposits on the surface of other stones, and immediately liked this visual and material contrast. This is how glass came to be so widely applied not

just to Skywalk's floors, but to its walls and walkway edges as well (see page 21), and how the rusting steel came to be used not just for the bridge elements, but also for guideways, coverings, roofs and even guiderails. With this, the core palette for the design was crystallized in the first hour the architect spent on site. As Sturgess explains: "We wanted materials and a layout that were clearly man-made but would fit cohesively into the landscape."

Now attention turned to the layout or spatial narrative—how the Skywalk bridge and its related elements would be first organized, then how they would sit on the landscape. Brewster's design brief asked that there be a number of interpretive visual and verbal displays to explain local flora, fauna and geology, but competing teams were given almost complete latitude about where and how these would be accommodated. Sturgess seized on the idea that these seemingly minor elements might be key to transforming the entire site into architecture, delivering a story on a grand scale to visitors through its visual forms. In Sturgess's words, shaping the arc of a narrative throughout

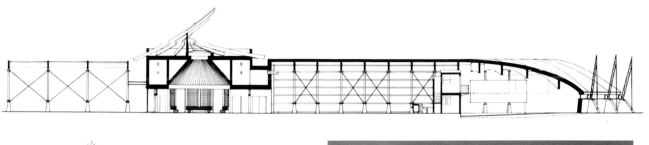

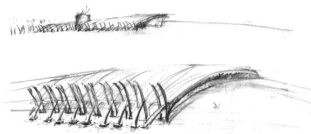

the entire site was critical: "We decided to design a circuit where
the pleasure of the glass walk would be extended and deferred."
This notion of a circuit of displays was an idea that Sturgess
Architecture (in association with FSC Groves Hodgson Manasc
Architects) had previously explored in the Yukon Visitor Reception Centre (now renamed the Beringia Interpretive Centre),
which won a Governor General's Medal in Architecture in 1997.
There, visitors pass from the parking area through a grove of
aspen trees into the boldly shaped building to view a series of
sequenced displays and engage in hands-on experiences, then
pass outside into a northern garden where a string of botanical
and geological interpretive elements are set on a meandering
path. However, rather than bunching them into a single
central building as in the Yukon, for Glacier Skywalk Sturgess
envisioned installing the interpretive materials along the way,
crafting a narrative journey to the cantilevered bridge and
amplifying the experience of the site. In other words, by taking
the displays entirely into the landscape—flanking the walk
from the drop-off point to the actual Skywalk bridge—architecture would actively inflect and define visitors' experience.

Sturgess further refined the design after a research trip to the glass-floored tourist observation platform on the south rim of the Grand Canyon in Arizona. He was disappointed by the way all of the interpretive material was consolidated into a vaguely adobe-style visitor centre and how the simple out-and-back loop layout reduced the visitor experience of one of the most dramatic natural landscapes on earth to a single-file shuffle around the glass floor that was over in minutes. What did impress him, however, was the simple and uncluttered cantilever of the Grand Canyon Skywalk. The sensation of floating above the valley with minimal supports was the key to the drama of the Glacier Skywalk experience. In the words of Dr. Simon Brown, RJC's lead on Glacier Skywalk's structural engineering team, "The most powerful way the project could interact with visitors would be to maximize the sense of exposure inherent in the site." This meant a glass floor for the entire bridge structure and a pure cantilever supported solely back into the rocks of the valley wall—no supports visible angling underneath or a ring of supporting cables tied to a column rising above the structure. The design solution from the RJC engineers was an ingenious set of two rings of bundled steel cables running around under the walkway—one in structural compression, the other in tension—that could be fine-tuned to make the bridge stable and comfortable for the public to use (see page 41).

In contrast to other traditional observation platforms such as the one at the Grand Canyon, Sturgess felt the walk over glass needed more drama than a simple and symmetrical

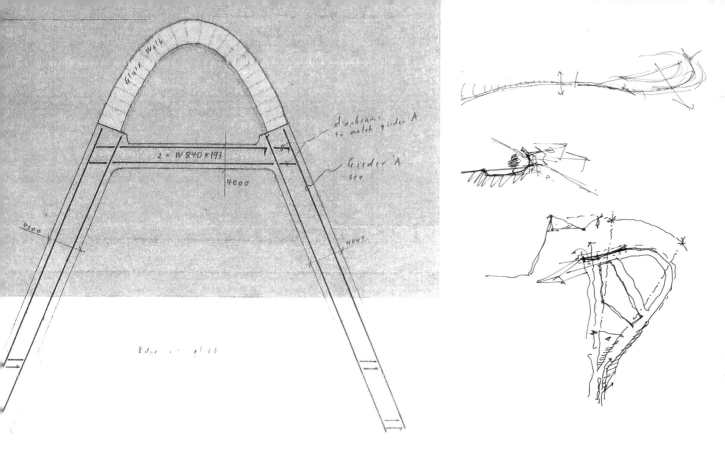

Glass Walk

2 × W 840 × 193

4000

4000

4000

diaphragms to match girder A

Girder 'A' sea

Edge of cliff

U-shaped horseshoe could provide, so he proposed making one side longer. "By rejecting the pure horseshoe shape and deforming the Skywalk bridge, we deflected it towards the most dramatic views," says Sturgess, "which has the added benefit of helping it fit more cohesively into the landscape." As well, a cross-bridge with a solid floor (instead of the laminated layered glass product used elsewhere) was added, spanning the two main sides for structural bracing. This cross-bridge also gave visitors a choice of routes to extend their experience of Skywalk. Thus, the most expensive and complex element of Brewster's Glacier Skywalk was shaped by the needs of narrative, not just by simple technical problem solving. "The scenography, the choreography of the visitor experience is the core of the reason our proposal won the competition," says the architect.

GLASS

GLASS was chosen for the floor, walls and handrails of the Skywalk bridge. Not only does it reference the calcified deposits on rocks on the mountainside, but the transparency of the glass challenges visitors and emphasizes the cantilever by exposing the structure and the view under the bridge to the valley below: a major aspect of the experience. From a distance, the glass appears to be extruded or erupted from the Cor-ten jaws that support it. / *c.s.*

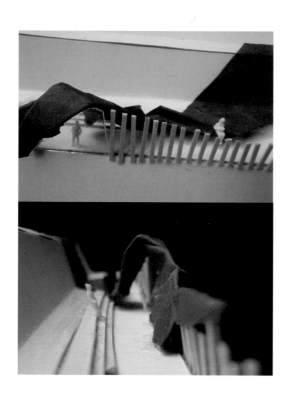

Early concept model in
paper, cardboard and wood.
Photo courtesy of Sturgess
Architecture

/ DEVELOPING THE DESIGN / With the concept in place, Sturgess/RJC/PCL were able to move to the next phase—design development—and complete their proposal for Glacier Skywalk. An integral part of the choreography involved using different architectural forms to help reveal the qualities of the site and to enrich the visitor's walk with the constructions themselves. In other words, the Glacier Skywalk experience is as much architectural as it is natural; it is defined as much through its constructions as through its museum-style explanatory panels.

Sturgess's "narrative architecture that instructs" comes from a long historical tradition. The unity of architectural forms with sculptural programs allowed the great medieval cathedrals to communicate the lessons of scripture and the lives of the saints to a largely preliterate public. Walking around and through a large Gothic church is to have architecture and its subservient arts help in moral and spiritual understanding. The Swiss-French modernist architect Le Corbusier returned to this notion of narrative architectural journeys in his later works, notably with the Dominican priory of Sainte Marie de La Tourette near Éveux, France. Here the architecture is shaped directly from the patterns and repetitions of liturgical texts, its very

rooms and corridors designed as a direct expression of
the daily rounds and prayers of the monks who live there.
It is a mnemonic aid to the Dominican's daily repetitions of
liturgical texts and rituals, enriching these acts of devotion.
Further amplifying Le Corbusier's ideas at La Tourette is the
musical pattern of windows and mullions, sequences of light
and dark established by Greek composer Iannis Xenakis to
enrich each monk's spatial journey. Le Corbusier's phrase for
this composition of architectural elements into a narrative
journey was *promenade architecturale*, and the notion informed
such later works as his Carpenter Center for the Visual Arts at
Harvard, with its pedestrian ramps up to and right through
the building, which afford casual passersby views into its
active studios and classrooms.

Locating its place in contemporary architectural culture,
Glacier Skywalk is a Corbusian *promenade architecturale*, a
passage through tectonic forms that enlightens and inspires.
The documentation of Sturgess's design sequence, seen
in an early cloth and wood conceptual model, then in an
early freehand concept plan, freehand sketches exploring

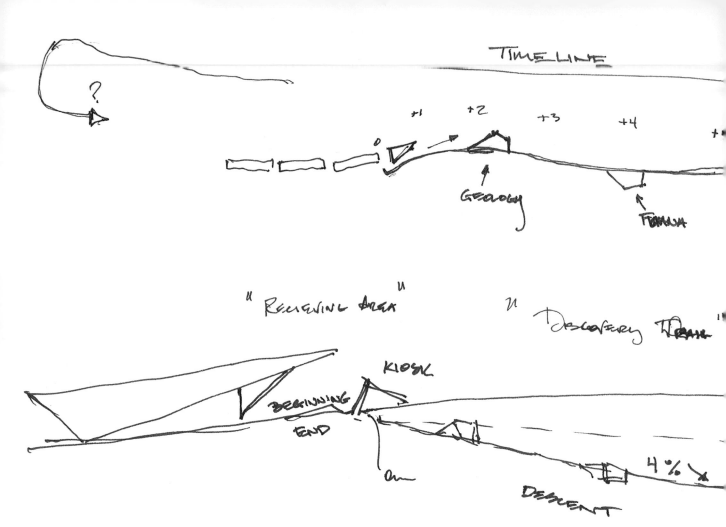

TIME LINE

+1 +2 +3 +4 +

0

GEOLOGY

FORMULA

"RECEIVING AREA" "DISCOVERY FRAME"

KIOSK

BEGINNING
END

on

DESCENT

4 %

Concept sketches showing the
promenade architecturale.

key features and ultimately measured engineered drawings,
graphically demonstrates the core notion of a string of
pavilions and display nodes along the narrative path.
The last major design development decision was to devise
specific shapes for these built elements. Sturgess felt the
particular shapes, especially the Skywalk bridge itself, should
represent the geological forces that had made the mountains:
"I wanted a series of fractal planes that seemed to extrude

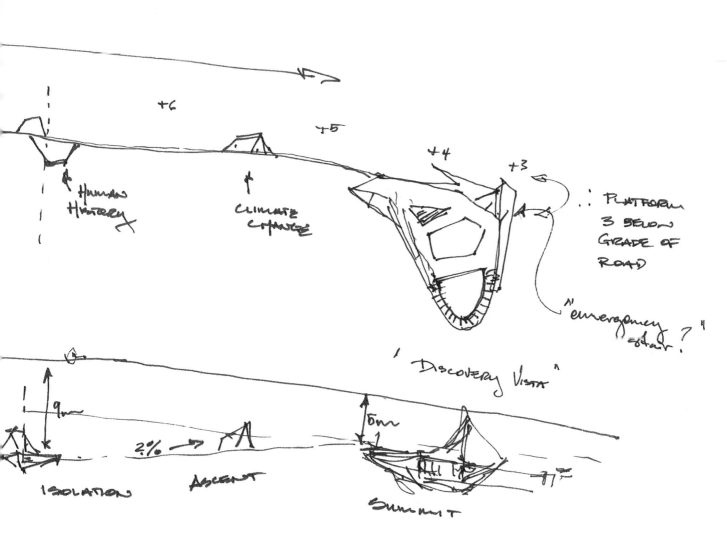

from the rocks, that would become markers of what the mountains could be." While the Cor-ten shapes evoke the forces behind mountain making, the designers held no aspirations for their architecture to directly imitate its surroundings: "We had no pretensions to being natural— we wanted a kind of fit for the angled Cor-ten planes, so that their artificiality would come to be seen as inevitable," Sturgess says.

At the start of the walk, for example, they planned a kiosk covered in larch boards but framed by welded and bent Cor-ten plate (see page 29). This kiosk manages to be both welcoming and unsettling, a warm greeting from an unusual but friendly emissary from another world. Sheltered sitting ledges are built in around its perimeter, but its interior spaces are for staff support and storage, with a chemical toilet "for emergency use only." Farther on is the first of the displays that the architects came to call interpretive nodes. These explain the wildlife of the area, the geology, and the design and construction ideas behind Skywalk, and each has its own distinct architectural form: bridge viewpoint; cave; archway; amphitheatre. Farther along, the frame of the gateway through which every visitor passes en route to the Skywalk bridge is Cor-ten steel formed into a gridded waffle structure and then wrapped with more Cor-ten. On a practical level, this rare bit of shelter on site can serve as refuge for visitors during short showers, which are not uncommon at this altitude. On an aesthetic level, the gateway isolates and frames particular views of the landscape on both the approach and the return. Finally, the jagged shape of the gateway visually expresses the geological forces that lift seabeds and forests and form them into mountains.

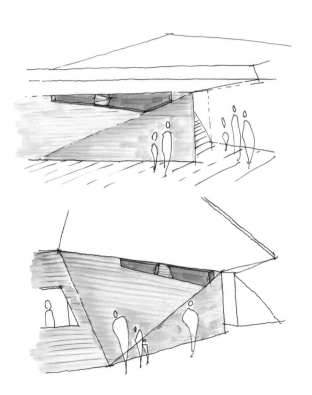

Concept sketches showing the kiosk, gateway and viewpoint.

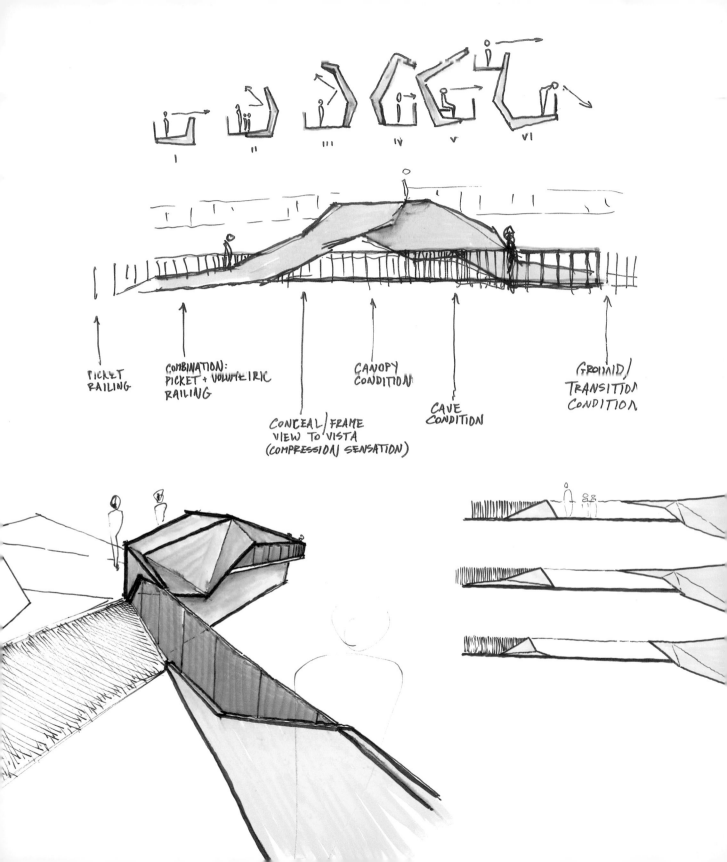

I II III IV V VI

PICKET
RAILING

COMBINATION:
PICKET + VOLUMETRIC
RAILING

CONCEAL/FRAME
VIEW TO VISTA
(COMPRESSION SENSATION)

CANOPY
CONDITION

CAVE
CONDITION

GROUND/
TRANSITION
CONDITION

WOOD

LARCH WOOD, harvested and milled in southeastern British Columbia, was chosen for the kiosk and the amphitheatre, where people sit and rest. It was specifically selected for its softness, colour and smell, which contrast with the hard, rugged surfaces throughout the site.
It is possible to sit at the apex of the amphitheatre in the afternoon sun and feel that you are on top of the world.
/ *c.s.*

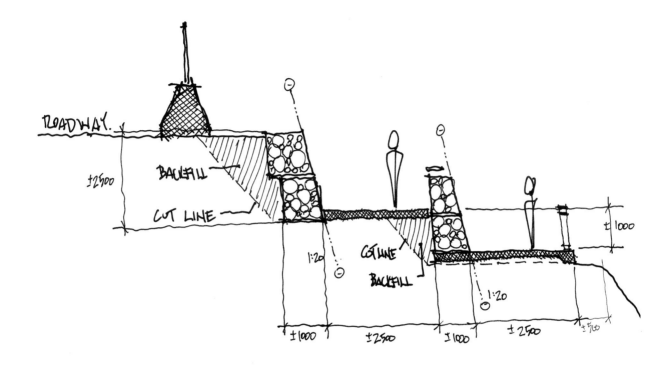

ROADWAY.
±2500
BACKFILL
CUT LINE
1:20
CUT LINE
BACKFILL
1:20
±1000
±1000
±2500
±1000
±2500
±500
±1000

Concept sketches showing
the pathways.

To visually balance the Skywalk, the smaller secondary
viewpoint (both cantilevered) and the various nodes, the
architects proposed a simple and powerful design that repre-
sents solidity, mass and resistance. There was a practical need
for stable retaining walls to protect the pedestrian walkways
across the site. These edges could have been constructed in
concrete, steel or even heavy wood. Instead, Sturgess was
drawn to a detail he had seen in a Herzog & de Meuron–
designed winery in Napa Valley and then again at a hotel in

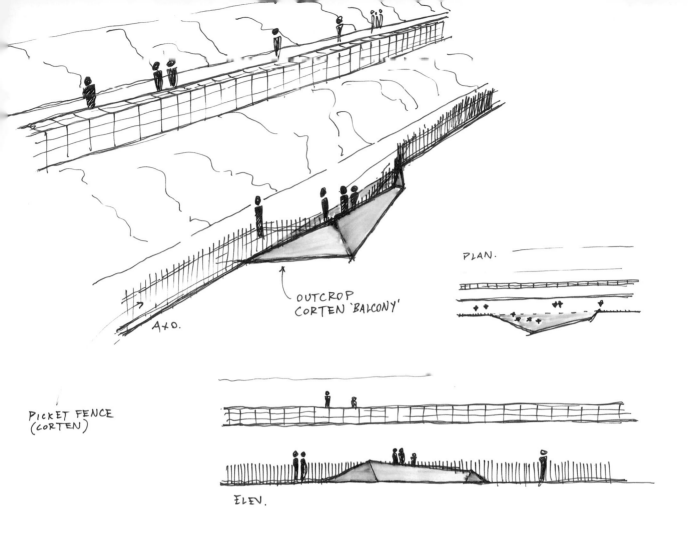

AXO.

OUTCROP
CORTEN 'BALCONY'

PLAN.

PICKET FENCE
(CORTEN)

ELEV.

Hamburg (see page 23): a gabion, a large volume of carefully
selected stones set within a gridded heavy steel mesh
(see page 33). Placed together, they would form a solid grey
wall, a visual counterpoint to the knife-like thrust of the
angled Cor-ten elements.

With the core ideas stable, the design elements drawn
and redrawn as their features evolved, Glacier Skywalk
was nearly ready to package into the final set of drawings,
renderings and verbal explanations.

STONE

LOCAL ROCKS mined as a result of site excavation and enclosed in steel mesh to make gabion baskets were chosen for the retaining walls that line the cliffside paths. Similar baskets are used to prevent landslides along the Trans-Canada Highway through the Rockies, but here rocks of 5 to 10 centimetres in diameter have been individually selected and placed by hand in finely honed steel mesh baskets to create pattern and rhythm in the solid stone wall. / *c.s.*

Competition renderings of
the kiosk and pathways.

/ **SUBMITTING THE WINNING ENTRY** / The submission took a month to finalize, once the team was assembled and the key architectural elements had been agreed upon and roughed out. Every element had to be designed to the point where it could be both costed and presented in an appealing package, and that process was complicated by knowing that Skywalk would need to be constructed for a fixed price during construction seasons sharply limited by both brief alpine summers and the kidding season for mountain goats from May to July. The team at Sturgess Architecture worked closely with the engineers at RJC and the builders at PCL to test,

revise and improve the design while preparing the final design–build documentation, which included a proposal outlining how it would be built, when final working and shop drawings would be submitted and, perhaps most importantly, what it would all cost.

The preparation of the Skywalk competition entry was made considerably easier by using the latest in building information system software, which allowed the builders, contractors, engineers, steel fabricators and architects— all located in different offices—to work from exactly the same three-dimensional drawings of every element in the

Competition renderings of the site and the Skywalk bridge.

buildings. In particular, Sturgess says his call for an asymmetrical shape for the Skywalk bridge would likely have been turned down by the builders and engineers had digital technology not made it so easy to work together on the structural and constructional complications this shape introduced. To build one of the most complex small constructions ever attempted in Alberta, the whole team had to feel confident.

In November 2010, Brewster announced that it had accepted the design proposal from the PCL/RJC/Sturgess team. The decision surprised the Alberta construction community, but the reception from the public and professionals

worldwide—even before construction commenced—was overwhelmingly positive. Glacier Skywalk was recognized with the Future Projects/Competition Award at the World Architecture Festival in Barcelona in 2011. The consensus was that Glacier Skywalk is architecture that is truly new—to the mountain parks and to the designers themselves. It is an impression that has been borne out with many subsequent awards: from *Architizer* magazine's Jury Award (voted on by architectural writers) and Popular Choice Award in 2015—a rare double win—to the prestigious Governor General's Medal in Architecture in 2016. //

Building
The Skywalk

THE GLACIER SKYWALK construction process had to be carefully planned to be as efficient as possible on a fixed budget and to minimize the impact on the environment. Skywalk sits on land previously disturbed during the construction of the Icefields Parkway, and Parks Canada had already designated the land for outdoor recreation to promote understanding, appreciation and enjoyment of the park's heritage.

But projects like this, involving cliffside excavation, wilderness conditions and steel cantilevers, are rarely undertaken, and the construction team had to consider many things it had never seen before.

The first plan was to build the whole thing in one season, which turned out not to be feasible for two reasons. First, the harsh winters limited the construction season to just six or seven months. Second, a wildlife impact study found that the kidding season for the mountain goats and bighorn sheep that live in the area takes place from May to July and that having people and equipment around at certain times would interfere with

SUSPENSION CABLE SYSTEM

To maximize the views and heighten the sense of exposure, the glass walkway was designed with a minimum of structural framing members by using a unique eccentric self-anchored suspension cable system. The result is that visitors feel as if they are floating in air over the valley floor, but the self-anchored cable system allows for the movement and vibration of the structure from both footsteps and wind loading.

that natural cycle. Fifteen cameras were set up around the site to monitor the animals' movements, and ultimately it was decided that Glacier Skywalk would have to be built between July and October only, over two alpine summers, and only outside of the morning and evening hours during which the goats use the area. The monitoring continued through the construction phase and is still ongoing. An environmental assessment study also reviewed the concept of Glacier Skywalk and its construction, ongoing operations, traffic management procedures and impact on wildlife and ecosystems, as well as the cultural history of the area and future requirements associated with the project.

A chain-link fence mitigated erosion during the construction phase. Photo courtesy of Sturgess Architecture

/ **SETTING THE FOUNDATION** / The construction crew began by building the major structural components—the platform foundation—including the steel girders that would support the structure of the Skywalk bridge. Initially, core samples of the rock were taken at four locations of the Skywalk site and visually inspected to review the rock quality. In the lab, the samples were tested for load (their ability to hold the weight of the structure), compressive strength (their ability to resist breaking when squeezed under load) and direct shear (their ability to resist breaking when squeezed in two opposing directions). Engineers also tested the strength of the rock samples to ensure that the cliff could support the weight of the Skywalk bridge.

Once the rock had been tested, construction began. Erosion-control equipment was installed on site to protect the existing rock bed, and an anchor chain-link fence and curtain were placed on the side of the cliff to prevent rocks from falling into the valley. Crews blasted rock out of the cliffside and drilled rock anchors into the ground. Once the foundation anchor rods—threaded bolts with a nut and washer at one end—were in place, foundation footings were formed to support the load and reinforcing steel was installed to strengthen the concrete. Stress plates were installed onto anchor rods to mitigate the stress of minor movements, and steel bearing plates were added. Concrete was then placed, finished and cured in one continuous operation.

While the foundation for Skywalk was being set, a demolition contractor drilled blasting holes 3 metres deep to form the pathways along the cliff, and the fractured and blasted rock was excavated from the foundation using a hydraulic excavator.

CANTILEVERED CONSTRUCTION

The 30-metre glass vista point rests 280 metres above Sunwapta Valley, at an elevation of 1,880 metres above sea level, and reaches 35 metres beyond the edge of the cliff. Glacier Skywalk is a cantilevered structure, which means it is anchored at only one end. There is no support either above or below the platform; it uses the rock bluffs as its only anchor. Two trapezoidal steel box girders, connected at their ends by a steel bridge, are fixed with high-strength bolts onto concrete foundation blocks. Thirty-four high-strength steel rods were drilled 16 metres into the cliff to anchor the foundation blocks securely to the bedrock.

VIBRATION DAMPERS

Skywalk has been built with four half-tonne tuned mass dampers—the four black boxes attached to the underside of the glass. They absorb the vibrations from pedestrian footfalls by dissipating kinetic energy to control the movement of the structure. Although these dampers also help to mitigate the vibration resulting from the valley's high winds, the shape of the glass walkway and the glass balustrades deflect most of the wind.

/ CRAFTING THE COMPONENTS /

Assembling a structure like Skywalk in such a small space required the design and engineering teams to work closely together before and throughout construction. This involved thinking through what could be built off site beforehand and how best to assemble the pieces at the site. The metal structure that underlies the glass walkway was prefabricated in pieces trucked into the future bus pull-off/ parking lot at the top of the site and welded together. All the welds were x-rayed and analyzed to ensure their integrity. Crews used a 318-tonne crawler crane and a Superlift lattice boom crawler crane to lift the massive pieces into place.

FROM LEFT TO RIGHT The gateway was crafted in pieces off site by Heavy Industries of Calgary; it was assembled on site in the parking lot; finally, it was lifted into place. Photos courtesy of Sturgess Architecture. FACING The four black boxes under the nose of the Skywalk bridge dampen the vibration from wind and walking. Photo courtesy of Les Constructions Beauce Atlas Inc.

The load-bearing structure of the bridge was transported as one unit on a low loader trailer from the pre-assembly area to the installation site 500 metres away and lifted into position in one piece.

After the bridge was bolted to its anchors and all bolt and screw connections had been closed, the bridge was lifted into the proper position so that the steel tension cables, located in the two large circular tubes behind the glass, could be inserted and tightened. After the pre-tension in all cables was uniformly adjusted, the bridge became self-supporting. And since the Skywalk bridge is extremely sensitive to vibrations due to the combination of the support structure's flexible joints, the pre-tensioned cables, the light construction and the exposed site in the high mountains, four mass vibration dampers were installed and blocked to the steel construction below the walkway to prevent the bridge from moving too much when people walk over it. After the glass floors and balustrades were installed, the vibration dampers were calibrated by means of sensors attached at various points along the bridge.

With the bridge installed, crews began bolting the Cor-ten steel cladding to each of the underlying steel components.

LOAD-BEARING GLASS FLOOR

Supported by the steel structure, the glass floor of the platform measures about 90 square metres and is made up of twenty-five glass panes. Each pane is supported on four sides by beams and measures about 2.6 × 1.2 metres. This floor is made up of four layers: the load-bearing glass consists of three 10-millimetre-thick heat-strengthened panes that are laminated together to form a single structural unit. The fourth layer is a 6-millimetre tempered glass sheet that is not bonded to the other layers. It is not required to support any weight; instead, it is designed to be replaced every few years as it becomes scratched from use. When it rains, a series of white dots (frit pattern) on the top sheet of glass helps prevent visitors from slipping. The total thickness of the glass platform is 4 centimetres. The total weight capacity of the glass is 81,000 kilograms.

Once the load-bearing portion of the Skywalk had been lifted into place with enormous precision and secured, the rest of the project was completed very quickly. Photo courtesy of Les Constructions Beauce Atlas Inc.

For example, adjacent to the rock wall, a structural steel framework was bolted to the structural steel trapezoidal girders. Once that framing was installed, Cor-ten was attached to the framework. As the cladding reached the rock wall, it was periodically adjusted to obtain an adequate fit. The kiosk and pathway, including the nodes, and the architectural features of the Skywalk bridge were built last.

After the complicated process of excavating, blasting and assembling the bridge, the rest of the project came together very quickly. //

Exploring The Skywalk

"WRITING ABOUT MUSIC IS LIKE dancing about architecture," declared actor Martin Mull, yet this string of pavilions, walkways and bridges above the Sunwapta Valley choreographs the visitor experience. From the arrival kiosk to the viewpoint to the cave, the gateway, the bridge and the amphitheatre, one is compelled to move, turn, bend and look to experience Glacier Skywalk. What is more, since both art forms consider the interaction of people in space, architecture has more in common with dance than it does with painting, theatre, or, yes, writing. So don your slippers, lace up your runners, strap on those high heels or go barefoot as you enjoy a steely samba above the vales of Jasper National Park.

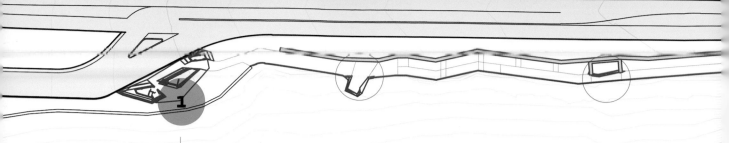

THE KIOSK

THE KIOSK pavilion at the bus drop-off lot is the gracious greeter, the warm and inviting introduction to the entire Glacier Skywalk site. It is clad in horizontal boards of larch wood, and the only other time this material appears is in the amphitheatre at the other end of the site. The kiosk fulfills a number of practical and aesthetic functions. Its angled walls are shaped into sheltered benches, providing visitors a place to rest while awaiting the return bus or to temporarily seek refuge from the short sun-showers that are a fact of the alpine climate. The entire site is off the electrical grid and has no water supply. Solar panels on the roof support equipment running within the kiosk. Inside the walls are storage space and a chemical toilet—"for emergency use only," as it is the only one on site. Some of the most important reasons for the kiosk are visual. The angled planes of Cor-ten introduce visitors to this particular building material plus give them a sample of Skywalk's general repertoire of visual forms. This introduction is important, because few will have seen Cor-ten steel so close up or welded and bent into so unusual a range of shapes. The building also serves as a screen, as visitors disembark from buses right in front of it, then walk around its edge, setting up the "awe" moment of seeing the pathway and its pavilions leading down to the thrusting metal and sparkling decks of the bridge itself.

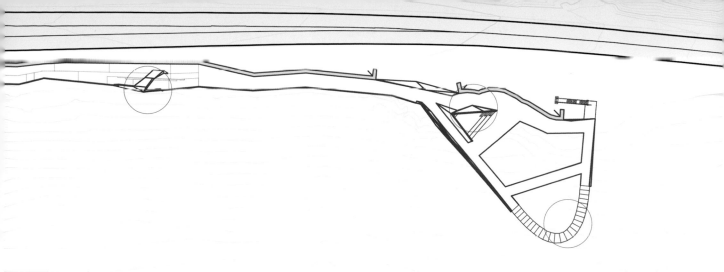

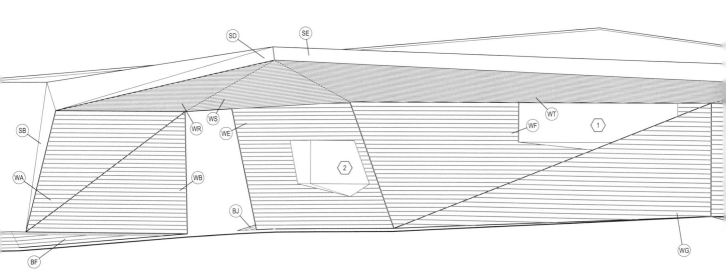

SD SE SB WS WR WE WT WF 1 WA WB 2 BJ WG BF

1 WEST ELEVATION
AK-13 SCALE : 1 : 50

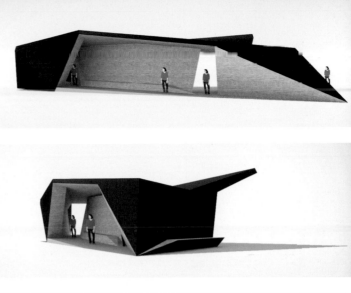

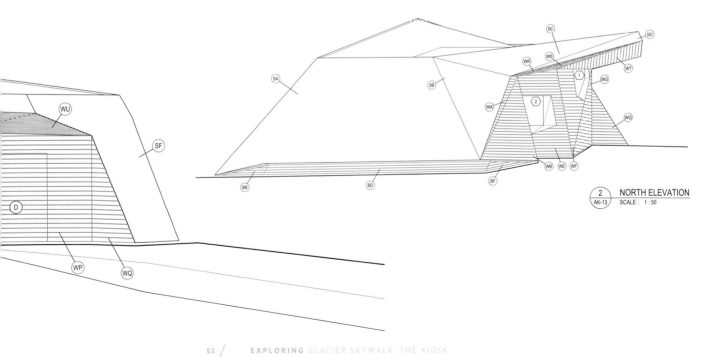

2 / **NORTH ELEVATION**
AK-13   SCALE : 1 : 50

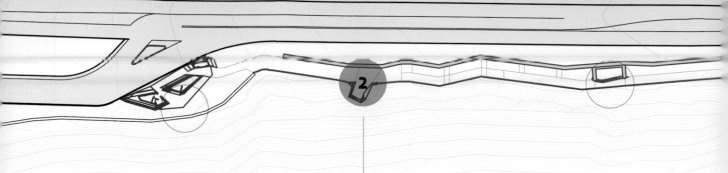

THE VIEWPOINT

After rounding the corner of the kiosk, the entire path down to the Skywalk bridge is visible. Most of the other pavilions (nodes) can be seen from this orientation point, introducing a storyline along the highway-side ridge. Seemingly small details like the handrails on the downslope side are carefully considered: they are angled posts crafted from Cor-ten with brackets supporting both a tubular steel handrail and cables strung from post to post. The first stop for most visitors is a small cantilevered bridge, which affords one of the most spectacular views of the main Skywalk. The importance of design is evident here: architecture provides a perch to view architecture, their common Cor-ten materials drawing into contrast the spectacular alpine valley all around them. This first viewpoint is a simplified miniature of the main Skywalk bridge. As such, it helps reassure visitors so they become bolder when they later encounter the longer cantilever and glass floors of the main bridge. There is an almost musical relation between the small and large bridges, like a sequence of notes first introduced with flute and cello, then repeated in symphonic majesty.

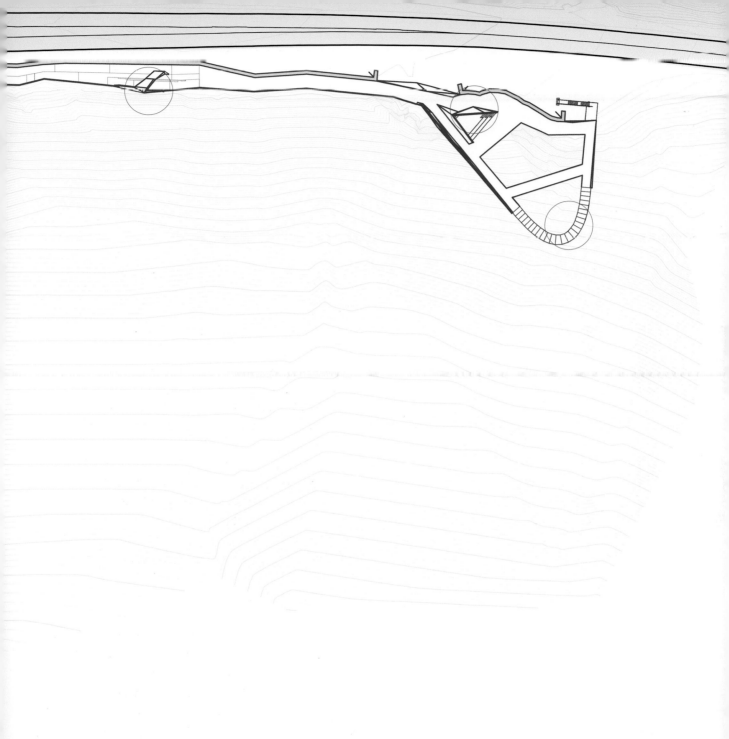

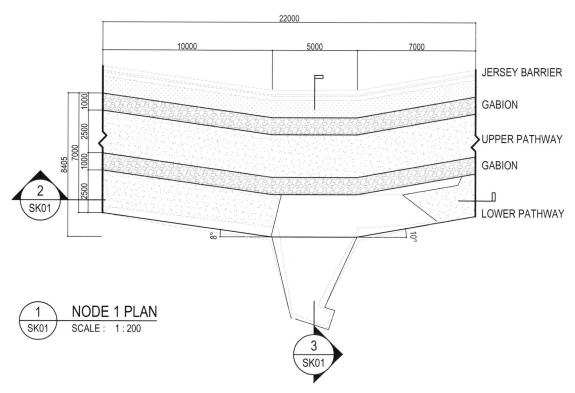

22000

10000   5000   7000

JERSEY BARRIER

GABION

UPPER PATHWAY

GABION

LOWER PATHWAY

1000
2500
7000
1000
2500

8405

8°

10°

2
SK01

3
SK01

1
SK01

NODE 1 PLAN

SCALE : 1 : 200

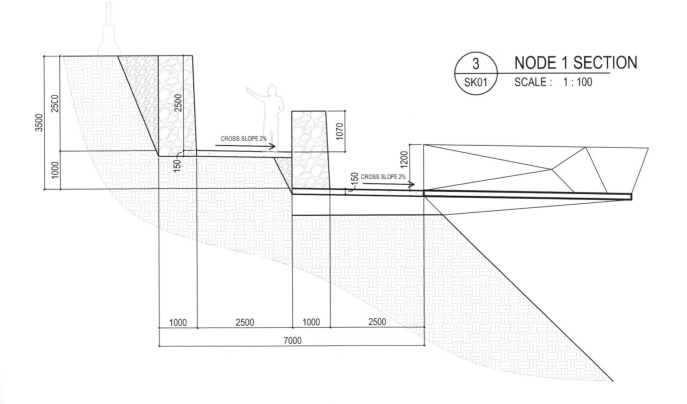

NODE 1 SECTION

3
SK01

SCALE : 1 : 100

CROSS SLOPE 2%

CROSS SLOPE 2%

3500

2500

1000

2500

2500

150

1070

150

1200

1000

2500

1000

2500

7000

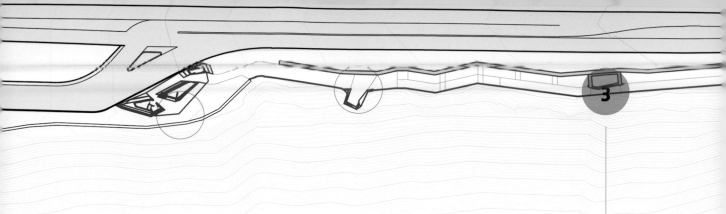

THE CAVE

Because the slope from the Icefields Parkway into the valley drops off fairly steeply, the pedestrian paths could not all be accommodated on the same level (it would have disturbed the site with too much excavation), so a loop was devised, with visitors returning on the higher level. The upslope walls lining these paths are constructed with gabion, selected rocks stacked within a metal grid box, which creates a stable retaining wall at a lower cost than cast concrete or steel walls. At one location, a niche with a multi-planed entrance made from Cor-ten gives visitors the option to step out of the flow of pedestrians and into the "cave" to read interpretive panels about the geology of the site. Extending these displays are fossil replicas cast into the concrete walkway (all paths are concrete to minimize tracking dirt and grit onto the Skywalk bridge's glass surfaces). For some visitors, this moment of repose from the unmediated exposure to raw nature—which can induce feelings of vertigo—is appreciated. The notion of Cor-ten representing the rocks and mountain-building forces is continued here, so the architecture itself is instructive.

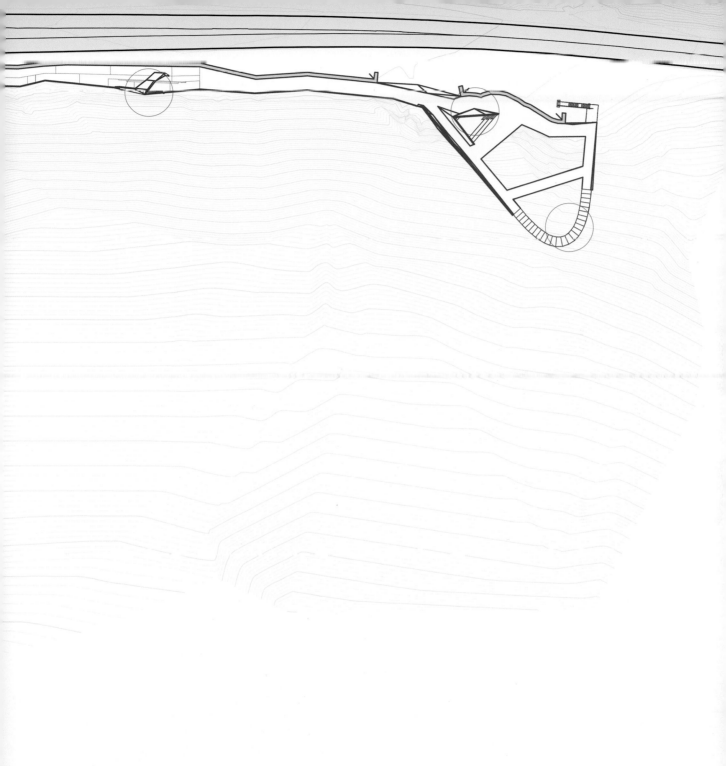

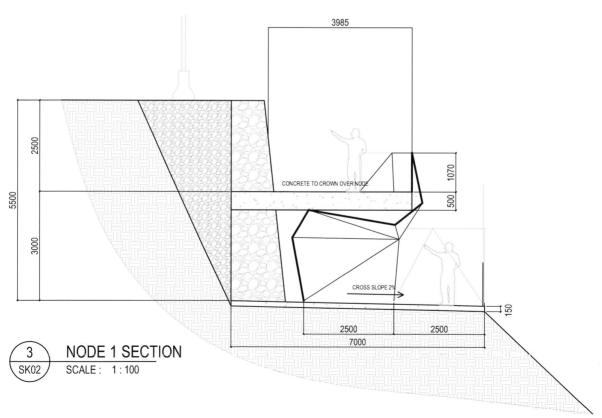

3985

2500

5500

3000

CONCRETE TO CROWN OVER NODE

1070

500

CROSS SLOPE 2%

150

2500 | 2500

7000

③ **NODE 1 SECTION**
SK02   SCALE : 1 : 100

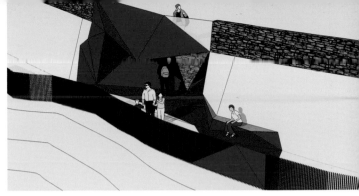

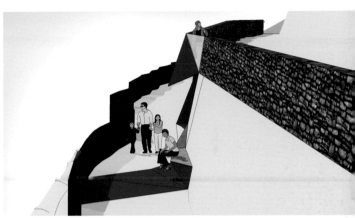

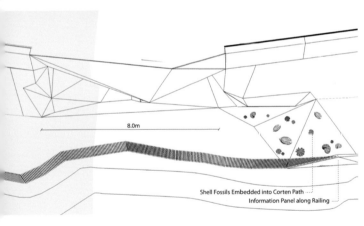

8.0m

Shell Fossils Embedded into Corten Path
Information Panel along Railing

THE GATEWAY
This node includes small panel displays about local fauna, such as bighorn sheep and mountain goats, grizzly and black bears, wolves and cougars. It is a popular and powerful way station on the approach to the Skywalk bridge, near the point where the paths to and from the Skywalk bridge come together again on the same level. Here, visitors arriving at the glass walkway see those just returning from their sometimes ecstatic experience, and the gateway visually frames these views towards the Skywalk bridge. While those leaving do not pass beneath it, the gateway is equally impressive in that direction, as it frames views of the pathways lined with gabion and Cor-ten retaining walls and visually isolates a vista of boulders and snowfields on a nearby mountain peak. The gateway itself is a marvel of ingenious construction, as pieces of Cor-ten steel have been welded to form a thick waffle-like gridded structure, which is then wrapped in Skywalk's signature angled Cor-ten steel plate. As they pass beneath the gateway on the way to the bridge, visitors sense the steel's weight and see in its rising and deformed shapes the upthrust of the tectonic plates that have shaped the surrounding mountains.

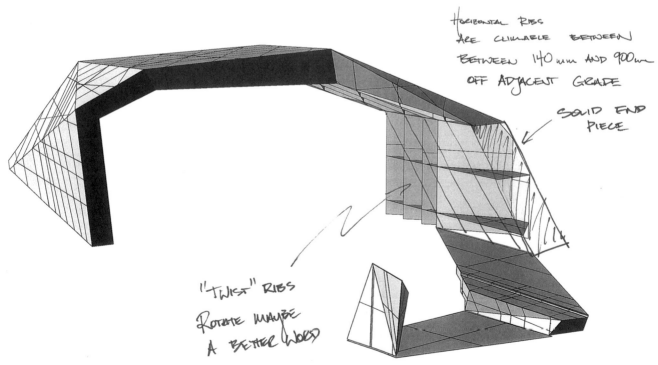

HORIZONTAL RIBS
ARE CLIMBABLE BETWEEN
BETWEEN 140 mm AND 900 mm
OFF ADJACENT GRADE

SOLID END
PIECE

"TWIST" RIBS
ROTATE MAYBE
A BETTER WORD

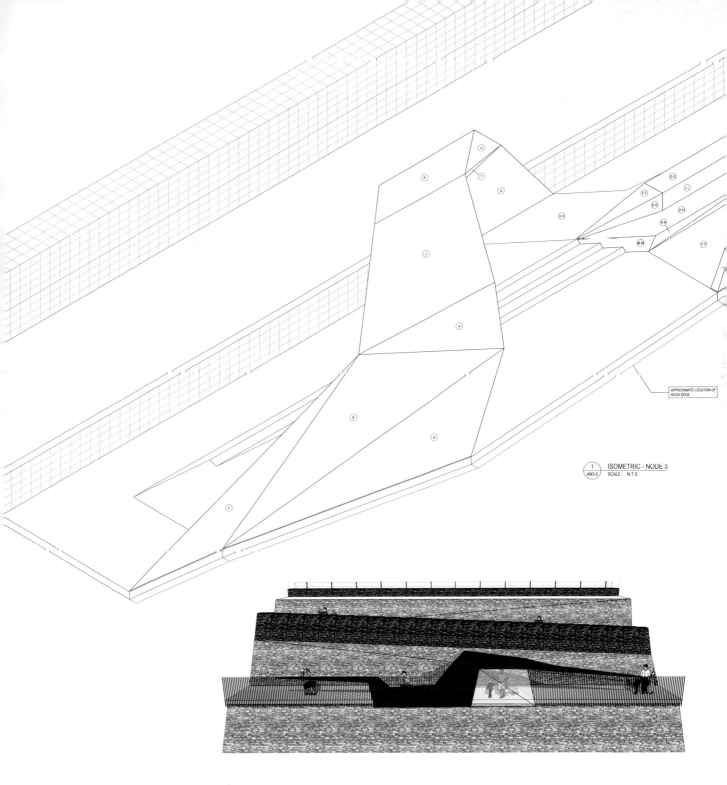

The added interpretive elements, such as these birds (fabricated by Global Experience Specialists Inc.), connect the architecture with its natural context. Photo courtesy of Sturgess Architecture

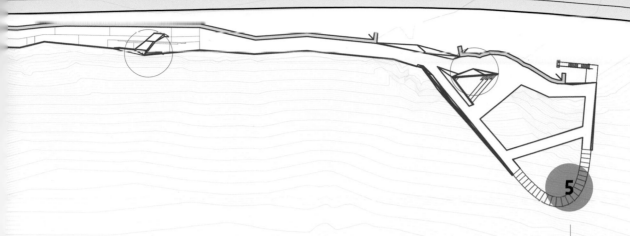

THE SKYWALK BRIDGE

Visitors know steel to be safe, strong and secure, which is one reason that it is used not just in the bridge structure but also along portions of the flanking walls and in the walkway posts. As they walk from the cliffside pathway onto the bridge, however, visitors start to see some changes. The steel cowlings that flank the path taper in height and then end before the rounded and most cantilevered "nose" section of the bridge. This architectural detail is psychologically reassuring because the cowlings initially provide a partial screen, a fade-in boundary, for those who might be shocked if the down-slope views were introduced all at once. Few notice that these cowlings were not built at the exit end of the bridge loop (they were a "value engineering" cut). Once people reach the glass-floored section, the straight secondary cross-bridge provides both structural bracing and an exit with a solid floor (a "chicken bridge") for those for whom the glass-floor vista is too much. Those who continue on the Skywalk bridge encounter a slight upslope as they approach the rounded end of Skywalk: it is useful for draining rainwater but also increases the visual drama. It gives the impression of standing on the prow of the bridge, hovering above the deep valley.

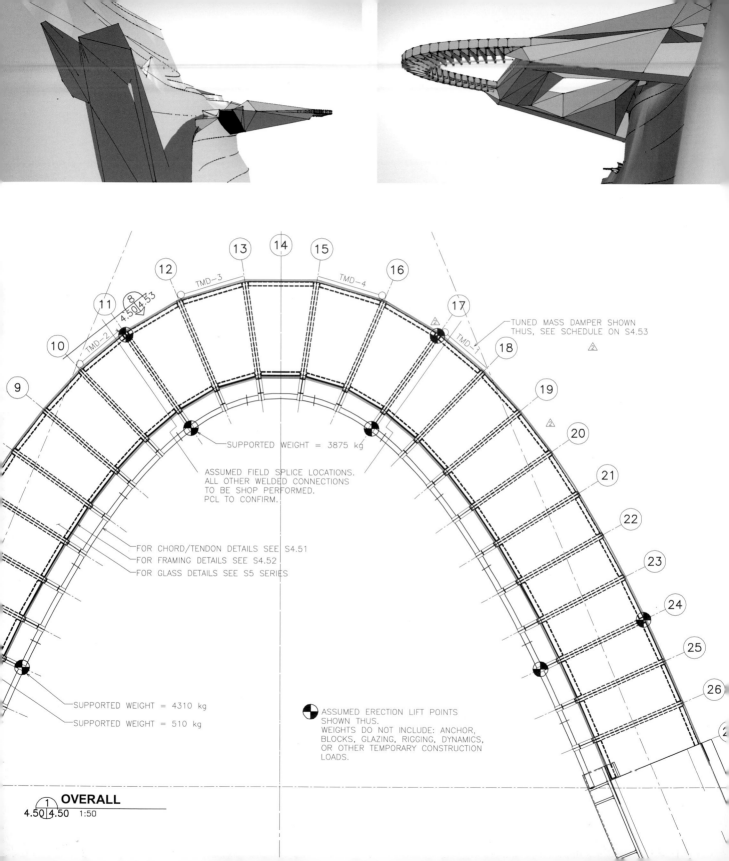

TMD-3

TMD-4

8
4.50 4.53

11

10

TMD-2

9

TMD-1

TUNED MASS DAMPER SHOWN
THUS, SEE SCHEDULE ON S4.53

SUPPORTED WEIGHT = 3875 kg

ASSUMED FIELD SPLICE LOCATIONS.
ALL OTHER WELDED CONNECTIONS
TO BE SHOP PERFORMED.
PCL TO CONFIRM.

FOR CHORD/TENDON DETAILS SEE S4.51
FOR FRAMING DETAILS SEE S4.52
FOR GLASS DETAILS SEE S5 SERIES

SUPPORTED WEIGHT = 4310 kg

SUPPORTED WEIGHT = 510 kg

ASSUMED ERECTION LIFT POINTS
SHOWN THUS.
WEIGHTS DO NOT INCLUDE: ANCHOR,
BLOCKS, GLAZING, RIGGING, DYNAMICS,
OR OTHER TEMPORARY CONSTRUCTION
LOADS.

1 **OVERALL**
4.50 4.50 1:50

The opening ceremony was attended by
representatives of Alberta First Nations
groups from Treaties 6, 7 and 8. Photo
courtesy of Sturgess Architecture

THE AMPHITHEATRE

is a somewhat deceiving name for this construction, as it is only infrequently used for formal talks or performances. The space is intended as a gregarious social area for visitors to sit, talk and otherwise compose themselves after completing the loop out onto the Skywalk bridge, where they had stood above the valley. Using the classic narrative of closing by return, the amphitheatre is clad in the same larch boards as the kiosk, a welcome and reassuring detail after all the strange angled planes of Cor-ten steel. The opaque steel perimeter walls are cut back and replaced by glass, though, so that those who are seated still have a view south along the Sunwapta Valley. The amphitheatre concludes the choreographed walk, with a unified aesthetic linking the nodes, pavilions and bridges that together form Glacier Skywalk's aerial ballet. Many visitors recharge here and then go back to experience the Skywalk bridge again, as people are welcome to stay at the site as long as they wish. //

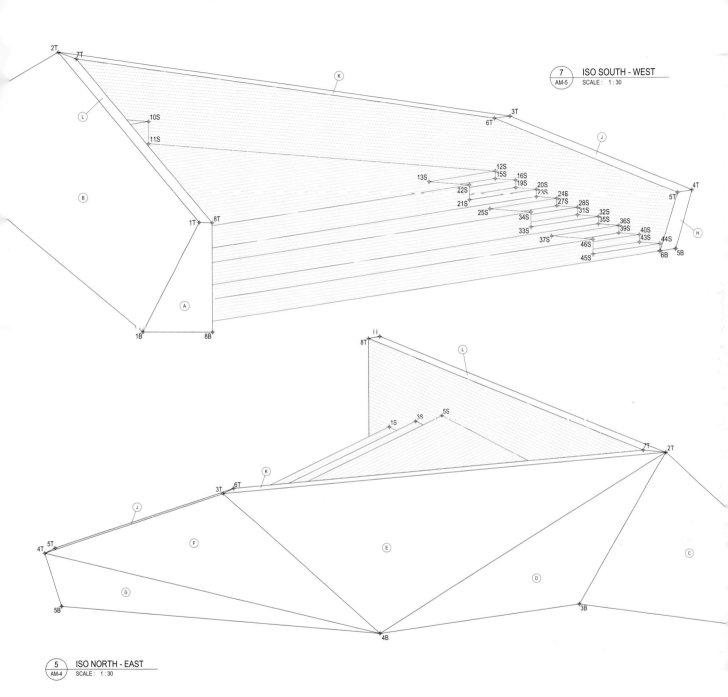

7 | ISO SOUTH - WEST
AM-5 | SCALE : 1 : 30

5 | ISO NORTH - EAST
AM-4 | SCALE : 1 : 30

Glacier Skywalk opened on May 13, 2014. The Reverb Brass
trio played in the amphitheatre at the opening ceremony.
Photo courtesy of Sturgess Architecture

Next
Skywalk

THE CREATION OF GLACIER SKYWALK is the culmination of a process and the beginning of a journey. My primary goal, with all of my work, is to create architecture that is evocative of its place and that fosters community. Our team researches local history and analyzes the topography to establish a working context that informs our expression for the site. We subjectively embrace the natural and the man-made interventions and weave our instinctive responses into the manifestation of the program, the built requirements for the project.

Working in the montane region of Canada has instilled in me a respect for the majesty of nature and a passion for the nuances of natural light and its impact on the planar surface. I recognize that the work must fit into the landscape—not as a replication of nature, but in harmony with the natural state. With this project, a design competition was held between teams of structural engineers, contractors and architects. We won the competition with an approach that offered a subtle but heroic intervention on the landscape, one that considered the experience itself as important as the destination.

Skywalk was originally planned as a horseshoe shape, the most efficient expression of the structural concept. We bent the horseshoe with one longer side to better engage the view of the glacier, and we created a series of fractal plates that welded the structure into the natural context.

We wanted to choreograph the visitor experience. Although the Skywalk bridge itself is the raison d'être, it is also just one aspect of the actual journey. We laid out a set of nodal experiences, the interpretive stations, to equip visitors to appreciate both the magnificent scenery and the reality of climate change. The site conditions inspired us to create this experience of discovery as a means to subtly and deliberately build the expectation for the ultimate moment—the Skywalk bridge.

The Skywalk experience affords options for exposure, appropriate to individual comfort levels. We tempered the level of bounce of the bridge dampers with a musician's metronome to achieve just enough frisson, or anxiety, related to the experience. Ultimately, after standing in mid-air, visitors can retreat to the amphitheatre, which offers a place to sit, a denouement for reflection and the opportunity to interact with fellow travellers.

An unprecedented level of collaboration was embedded in our design team. The contractor was a mountain climber who scaled the site before the design began, the structural engineer a genius in dynamic simplicity, the subcontractors artists in their realms. Together we worked seamlessly and iteratively amidst the daily realities of the design and construction process to realize the built work.

The successful completion of Glacier Skywalk will push our architecture further into the exploration of form and materiality in our commitment to respond to local context. We are excited by the opportunities that digital modelling and the iterative relationship between design concept and execution now afford. Every new project is a journey unchartered, an exploration into the unknown. We strive to discover and grow through these journeys, and consequently to define a new architecture that responds to the human condition, fosters community and celebrates place. //

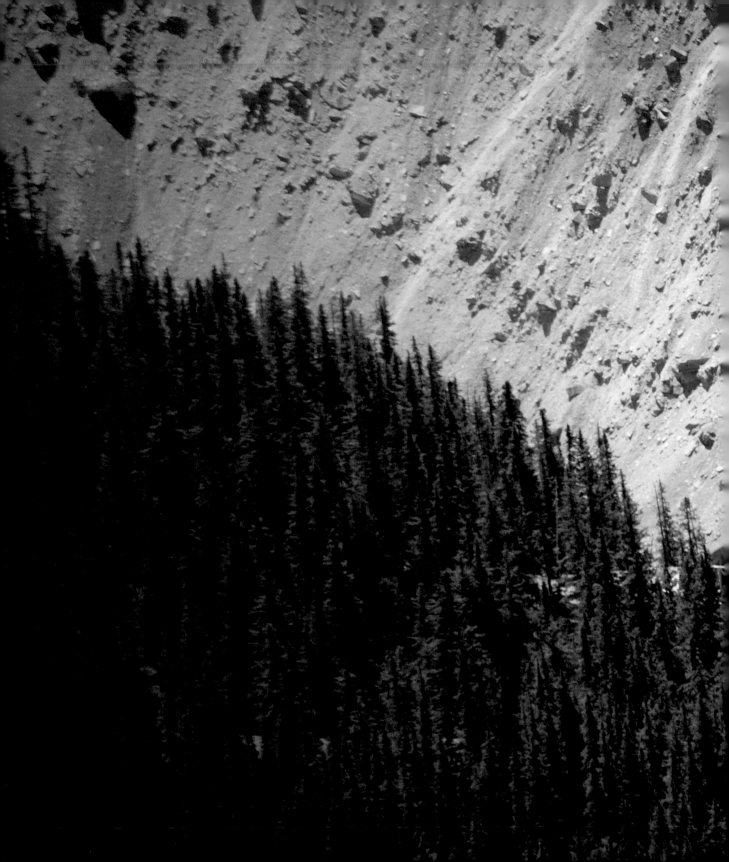

2016   Governor General's Medal in Architecture

2015   Steel Edge Award, Canadian Institute of Steel Construction, Alberta Region

2015   Award of Excellence, Special Applications, Post-Tensioning Institute Awards

2015   Award for Projects outside Quebec, Canadian Institute of Steel Construction, Quebec Region

2015   Architecture + Engineering A+ Award, Jury winner, *Architizer*

2015   Architecture + Engineering A+ Award, Popular Choice winner, *Architizer*

2014   Award of Excellence, Canadian Consulting Engineering Awards

2014   Best Paper Award, International Conference on Short and Medium Span Bridges

2014   Award of Excellence, Building Engineering, Consulting Engineers of Alberta Showcase Awards

2014   Award for Commercial/Institutional Projects, Canadian Institute of Steel Construction, Quebec Region

2014   Award for Stairs/Architectural Walkways, Canadian Institute of Steel Construction, Quebec Region

2014   Award of Excellence, Canadian Design-Build Institute

2014   Award of Merit for Environmental Assessment and Monitoring, Consulting Engineers of Alberta Showcase Awards

2013   People's Choice Award, *Alberta Construction Magazine* Top Projects Awards

2013   Top Commercial Project under $50 million, *Alberta Construction Magazine* Top Projects Awards

2013   Top Design, *Alberta Construction Magazine* Top Projects Awards

2011   Future Projects Category Winner, World Architecture Festival

STURGESS ARCHITECTURE

Sturgess Architecture is an award-winning Calgary-based design firm, celebrating almost forty years of architecture and urban design. A collaborative of architects, designers, technologists and assistants, the firm operates as a studio office, where all members of the staff are involved in the different phases and details of every project.

Sturgess Architecture is highly regarded for its collaborative skills, acting as lead architectural designer for such seminal projects as The Bridges Masterplan, the Yukon Visitor Reception Centre, the Seventh Avenue LRT Renewal, the Calgary Water Centre and the Calgary Green Line LRT.

Throughout its history, Sturgess Architecture has created a varied and interesting body of work, which was illustrated in *Full Spectrum,* a book published by University of Calgary Press in 2010. The firm's projects have won national and international recognition, including the 2011 World Architecture Festival award for Glacier Skywalk, which entered Sturgess Architecture into the league of the world's most innovative and celebrated architects.

BREWSTER TRAVEL CANADA

In 1892, two sons of an early pioneer to the Canadian Rockies trained through the First Nations people of the area and began guiding guests of the Banff Springs Hotel to scenic highlights in and around Banff National Park. In 1969, the company began operating Columbia Icefield snowmobile tours. Improvements in design resulted in today's unique, all-terrain Ice Explorers, which carry passengers in safety and comfort onto the Athabasca Glacier. Brewster Travel Canada is now a wholly owned subsidiary of Viad, a publicly traded company.

Today, Brewster welcomes more than 1.5 million guests and employs over 300 people annually through its tourism businesses. The head office is located in Banff, with satellite offices in Lake Louise and Calgary. The key to this entire legacy is Brewster's respect for the landscape. Throughout more than a century of operating in the magnificent Canadian Rockies, Brewster has adopted and respected Parks Canada's vision of forging healthy relationships between people and nature. In 1992, along with celebrating Brewster's 100th anniversary, Parks Canada cited the company for its century-long commitment to communicating national park values.

Brewster believes in community, service, quality and innovation. It takes pride in its historic origins in Banff and its focus on developing high-quality tourism products through time and experience.

BREWSTER TRAVEL CANADA PRESIDENT:
Dave McKenna

BREWSTER TRAVEL CANADA VICE-PRESIDENT OF OPERATIONS:
Stuart Back

BREWSTER TRAVEL CANADA DIRECTOR OF ENGINEERING:
Markus Reimann

COLUMBIA ICEFIELD— GENERAL MANAGER:
Rusty Noble

COLUMBIA ICEFIELD— DIRECTOR OF GUEST EXPERIENCE:
Steve McFadden

READ JONES CHRISTOFFERSEN (RJC) CONSULTING ENGINEERS

Read Jones Christoffersen Ltd. (RJC) specializes in structural engineering, parking facility design, structural restoration, building science, and structural glass and facade engineering services. Based in Canada, RJC has delivered such projects as bridges, hospitals, office and residential towers, airports, education facilities, parking structures and cultural facilities across the country and around the world.

The firm was founded in 1948 with a philosophy of focusing on clients a focus that has not wavered. Helping clients realize their vision for outstanding built environments is what RJC does. Organized, efficient, reliable, solid: just some of the words clients use to describe the value that RJC's service focus adds to their projects.

As leaders, RJC's people thrive on creativity. RJC's staff includes some of the industry's pre-eminent engineers and leading technical experts. The firm is committed to advancing fields of engineering expertise, a commitment emphasized through ongoing skills development—particularly through the mentorship of technical specialists—as well as ongoing involvement in associations, committees and the development of local, national and international codes, standards and protocols.

PCL CONSTRUCTION MANAGEMENT INC.

PCL is a group of independent construction companies that carries out work across Canada, the United States, the Caribbean and Australia. These diverse operations in the civil infrastructure, heavy industrial and buildings markets are supported by a strategic presence in thirty-one major centres. PCL celebrated its 110th anniversary in 2016.

The project team.

PROJECT CREDITS (in alphabetical order)

**COMPANIES INVOLVED
IN THE PROJECT**

AGF—Alberta Rebar Inc.

Alpine Land Surveys Ltd.

Apex Tile and Flooring Ltd.

BAT Construction Ltd.

Bluebird Contracting Services Ltd.

Bova Steel Inc.

Brewster Travel Canada

Buckland & Taylor Ltd.

Calibre Coatings Ltd.

CDJL Inspections en Soudage Inc.

Dynamic Concrete Pumping Inc.

Ferguson Corporation

Gabion Wall Systems Ltd.

Global Experience Specialists Inc.

Heavy Industries Theming Corporation Ltd.

Imperial Inspection & Consulting Ltd.

Josef Gartner Canada, a division of Bleu Tech
   Montreal Inc.

Lawson Projects Ltd.

Les Constructions Beauce Atlas Inc.

Mammoet Canada Western Ltd.

Oskar Construction Ltd.

Pacific Blasting & Demolition Ltd.

PCL Construction Management Inc.

Pro Line Pavement Markings Inc.

Read Jones Christoffersen Ltd.

Rite-Way Fencing Ltd.

SAHURI + Partners Architecture Inc.

SkyFire Energy Inc.

Skyline Building Envelope Solutions Ltd.

Skyline Roofing Ltd.

SMP Engineering

Sturgess Architecture

Thermal Systems KWC Ltd.

Thurber Engineering Ltd.

Urban Systems Ltd.

**DESIGN AND
CONSTRUCTION TEAM**

James Andalis

Jessie Andjelic

Lesley Beale

Keith Bowers

Simon Brown

Robbe Drugmand

Jennifer Drysdale

Elayna Ducharme

Joe Falica

Michael Farrar

Stefan Franke

Ryan French

Carla Grey

Anita Gunther

Devin Harding

Kevin Harrison

Jimmy Hoang

Bob Horvath

Josh Hughes

Geoff Kallweit

Dalton Kaun

Matthew Kennedy

Tanya Kennedy Flood

Baird Kerr

Khuyen Khuong

Jan Kroman

Matt Lamers

Krista Lauridsen

Larry Marasigan

Jenna Ogston

Shane Oleksiuk

Modesto Orizzonte

Amanda Parkinson

Tommy Ponton

Mark Ritchie

Amanda Robertson

Dick Rogerson

John Rust

Mariella Salas

Daniel Saraceni

Scott Schmold

Rachael Shemeliuk

Wade Straka

Clea Sturgess

Jeremy Sturgess

Mike Taylor

David Tyl

Scott Updegrave

Jessica Von Bachelle

Norm Webster

Dustin Worts

Annie Wright

ACKNOWLEDGEMENTS

Greg Fenton and all
   Parks Canada staff

Michael Hannan

Juliette Recompsat

Reverb Brass:
   Luise Heyerhoff
   Jonathan Rowsell
   Micajah Sturgess

SPECIAL THANKS

Derek Besant

Keith Bowers

Anne Brouillette

Simon Brown

Tanya Kennedy Flood

Scott Updegrave

Edmonton-born TREVOR BODDY is a critic of contemporary architecture and a consulting urban designer. His writing on buildings and cities has been awarded the Alberta Book of the Year Prize, a Western Magazine Award, the Royal Architectural Institute of Canada's Advocacy Award, a fellowship in New York's Institute for Urban Design and an honorary membership in the American Institute of Architects. At the 2011 World Architecture Congress in Tokyo, Boddy's essay (for *A/V* in Madrid) entitled "MEGA + MICRO: Canada, Innovation at the Extremes" received commendation for the UIA/CICA's Pierre Vago Prize for best architectural criticism published worldwide. As a curator, Boddy produced the Vancouverism: Architecture Builds the City exhibition plus the linked Trafalgar Square demonstration construction (named marquee event for the 2008 London Festival of Architecture), which was remounted in 2009 in Paris and then in Vancouver for the 2010 Olympics. Previously, Boddy taught architecture and urban design at the University of British Columbia, the University of Manitoba, the University of Oregon, the University of Toronto and Carleton University. He is based in Vancouver, British Columbia, and currently serves as a studio critic and lecturer worldwide. www.trevorboddy.ca.

CLEA STURGESS has been a writer and an editor of architectural texts for the past twelve years. She lives in Victoria, British Columbia, where she is currently pursuing graduate studies at the University of Victoria.

JEREMY STURGESS creates architecture that responds to
its site and is responsible to an overarching philosophy of
urban design. With every work, he attempts to instill an
aspect of community, to foster interaction between people
in a manner that will enrich and influence their experience
together. Whether in the city or in the natural environment,
he endeavours to create work that enhances the place
and enlightens the spirit. He has been recognized locally,
nationally and internationally for his work and is a member
of the Royal Canadian Academy of Arts, a fellow of the
Royal Architectural Institute of Canada and a recipient
of the Queen's Jubilee Medal in recognition of the artistic
quality of his work. He lives in Calgary, Alberta.

ROBERT LEMERMEYER specializes in architecture and travel
photography. His assignments have taken him to China,
Japan, the United States, Russia, South Africa, Chile, the
United Kingdom, Ireland and Israel. His work is inspired
by his ability to think like an architect. He frames every
image—from a house to an office building, from an avant-
garde hotel to a shanty—in thought-provoking ways that
tell a story through subtle touches of movement, colour and
light. A global nomad, curiosity seeker and citizen of the
world, Lemermeyer lives in a house on a hilltop with his wife
and two children in Calgary, Alberta. www.lemermeyer.ca.

// To listen to "Views-Trio," which was commissioned for the opening of Glacier Skywalk, written by Micajah Sturgess and performed by the Reverb Brass trio (see page 96), go to https://soundcloud.com/micajahsturgess/views-trio

Page xii map data © 2016 Google, imagery © 2016 Cnes/Spot Image, DigitalGlobe, Landsat, Parks Canada, Province of British Columbia

Photographs on pages 66–67, 78–79, 82–83, 86–87, 89, 90–91 courtesy of Brewster Travel Canada

Photographs on pages vi–vii, 102–107 by Terry Bourque Photo

Photograph on page ii–iii courtesy of Whyte Museum of the Canadian Rockies, Byron Harmon Fonds (V263 / NA-1821), whyte.org

17 18 19 20 21 5 4 3 2 1

Cataloguing data available from Library and Archives Canada
ISBN 978-1-927958-99-5 (pbk.)

Editing by Lucy Kenward
Copy editing by Lana Okerlund
Proofreading by Renate Preuss
Design by Natalie Olsen
Printed and bound in China by C&C Offset Printing Co., Ltd.

Figure 1 Publishing Inc.
Vancouver BC Canada
www.figure1pub.com